Bunny L
Others

written by Dr. Mary Manz Simon
illustrated by Dorothy Stott

© 2003 Mary Manz Simon. © 2003 Standard Publishing, Cincinnati, Ohio. A division of Standex International Corporation. All rights reserved. Sprout logo is a trademark of Standard Publishing. First Virtues™ is a trademark of Standard Publishing. Printed in Italy. Project editor: Jennifer Holder. Design: Robert Glover and Suzanne Jacobson. Scripture quoted from the *HOLY BIBLE, Contemporary English Version.* Copyright © 1995 by American Bible Society. Used by permission. ISBN 0-7847-1409-6

09 08 07 06 05 04 03   9 8 7 6 5 4 3 2 1

Standard
PUBLISHING
CINCINNATI, OHIO

www.standardpub.com

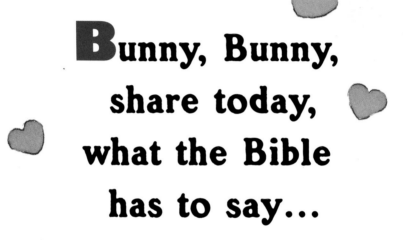

Bunny, Bunny, share today, what the Bible has to say…

**God is love.
It all starts there,
with our Father's
gentle care.**

GOD LOVES YOU

Then because
God loves me so,
I want all
the world to know!

Love shows in
my smiling face,
when I fill
a flower vase.

When I bring
a gift to share,
that will show
my love and care.

This is one thing
that I know:
it is fun
to watch love grow.

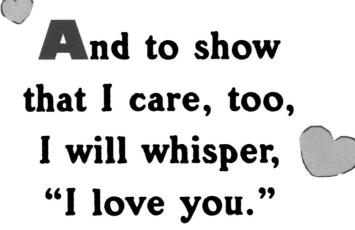

And to show
that I care, too,
I will whisper,
"I love you."

God shows love
to me each day.
That is why
I smile and say...

God is love.
He cares for you.
Will you share
his love now, too?

"Love God and love each other!"
1 John 4:21

Love Love Love Love Love Love Love Love Love

Love Love Love Love Love Love Love Love Love

Love Love Love Love Love Love Love Love Love

Love Love Love Love Love Love Love Love Love

Love Love Love Love Love Love Love Love Lov

Love Love Love Love Love Love Love Love Lov

Love Love Love Love Love Love Love Love Lov